Breath Energy Work
Exercises for the Mind & Body

Michael Holland

Published by Michael Holland
323 Ridgeland Avenue
Decatur, Georgia 30030

Copyright ©2008 by Michael Holland

Library of Congress Control Number: 2008905239

ISBN 978-1-60643-126-9

Printed in the United States of America

Photography by Michael and Miriam Holland
Cover design by Michael Holland

Acknowledgments

I would like to thank my wife, Miriam, director of Mei Zhong Yang Style Taijiquan Association, USA, and my son, Christopher—they've always been supportive, helped me get this done, and I love them; my mother, Lori Johnson, whose creativity has touched and inspired me; my sister, Vicki Warner, who understands me; my brother, Guy Katich, who got me to believe in the impossible; special thanks to my teacher, Shifu Cui Zhongsan, Fifth Generation Yang Style Master, for his knowledge, humor, willingness, and ability to transmit his special skills, Taiji and Qigong; Dr. Tingsen Xu, for the "longevity exercises" and introduction to the Chinese culture; Shifu Gary Mitchell, for teaching me the meaning of Gong Fu, hard work and accomplishment; John Crewdson, for showing me how to get it done, and helping me to do it; Ellen Glass, for her advice on graphics and proofreading; and Dr. Rick Agel, for sharing his medical knowledge and Qigong skills.

Contents

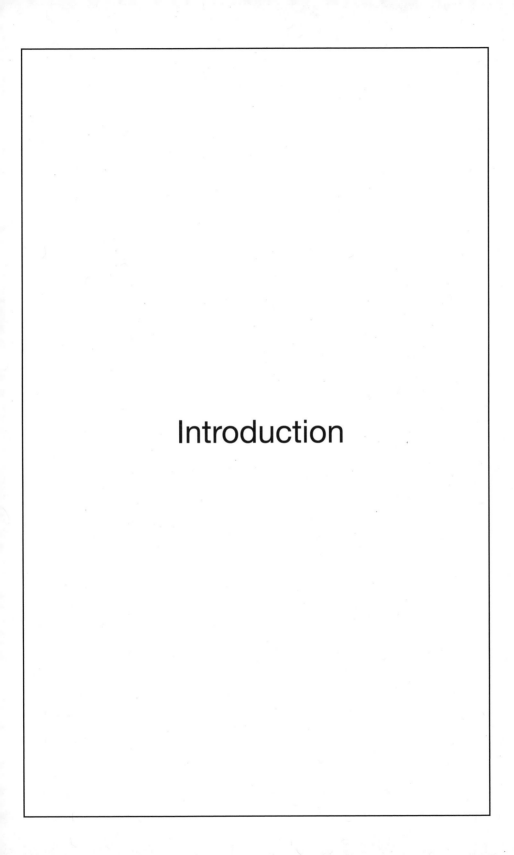

Introduction

In 1996, I was studying Taiji (Tai Chi) with Dr. Tingsen Xu. He had just come back from Shanghai and shared some hand movements with his Saturday morning class. He said that during his flight, an elderly Taiji Master sat next to him and showed him the "Longevity Exercises." It was a form of tapping that hit different meridian points on the hands. The elderly Master said that if you did them three times a day, you would live longer. Well, I'm not so naive that I immediately bought into this, but I started doing them just in case they worked. That was the beginning of my morning routine. My second Taiji/Qigong teacher, fifth-generation Yang Style Shifu (Master) Cui Zhongsan, who lives in Beijing, showed me more hand exercises, and the morning routine grew. Year after year, Shifu Cui has shared more of these hand exercises with me, along with Taiji and Qigong. I began to combine these exercises into a morning routine that would prepare me for the day, improve and maintain my health, and augment my Taiji practice.

There are millions of people in China who practice these types of exercises daily, and have been for over 4,000 years. I've seen 90-year-olds in China move better than 40-year-olds in America. There is a group of people in China, cancer survivors, who have extended their lives through regular Qigong practice. I know Americans who have reduced or eliminated the need for prescription drugs. Taiji and Qigong are preventive medicine. Whether you are in good health, concerned about work or life related stress affecting your health, or already in need of additional exercise to repair your health, these exercises have been proven to help. It all begins when you take the first step, deciding to try it, committing to regular practice, and doing it! The benefits will follow.

Practicing first thing in the morning is my preference; it's a great way to start the day. Begin in bed, if you like, and work your way up. The routine does not require any special equipment or a large space. This means you can do many of the drills at work or on your travels. For those of you who like to do more strenuous forms of exercise, use this as a warm-up. Many of my students claim they experience benefits such as greater lung capacity, reduced blood pressure, relief from cramping in the hands, better sleep, improved circulation, relief from stiffness, and stress reduction.

The tricky part is getting yourself to practice regularly. Once you begin the routine, it's easy to keep going. Decide on the best time for you, the amount of time you want to practice, and build on that.

In the first section of this book, you'll learn the hand work. You can do these first thing in the morning, in the car (if you're not driving), at work, or anytime. The face washing can follow the hand work (my preference) or be done in the shower. If you do face washing later in the day, be sure to wash your hands first. As you follow the rest of the routine, adapt it to fit your needs.

Begin with a short practice and gradually add on as you build up stamina. Your routine can be from five minutes to an hour. Repetition is the mother of skill, so be consistent. Five to ten minutes of practice daily is better than thirty minutes once a week.

A Taiji teacher I once met said, "Learning Taiji was like going to heaven. Everyone wants to go there, just not right now." So start out with good practice habits and not just good intentions. The art of gaining mastery over yourself, to get going with the things you want and need to do, is a very empowering experience. The dictionary says that *practice* is: 1. The actual application or use of an idea, belief, or method as opposed to theories about such applications or use; 2. Repeated exercise in or performance of an activity or skill so as to acquire or maintain proficiency in it.

I recommend you designate a place to practice. Mine is at the foot of the bed, looking out the window. I have tailored this curriculum to conform to a small space. This way you can do it at home or anywhere else.

Make your place of practice special. For example, I put a small Persian rug in my practice area. You might want to put up a Chinese scroll, play music, make it an atmosphere that helps nourish your practice. Also, when appropriate, practice outdoors. As you increase your knowledge and understanding of how these exercises work, it becomes easy to include them in your lifestyle, in all that you do. I've practiced in parking lots, on tennis courts, in hotel rooms, in mini gyms, on airplanes, on beaches, and in the parks of Beijing.

The Benefits

How would you like to: Reduce *both* systolic *and* diastolic blood pressure? Increase joint flexibility and deep muscle relaxation? Boost your immune system against shingles and possibly other viruses? Scientific studies have shown Taiji and Qigong to be effective in all of these areas.

Additional scientific studies have found that regular Taiji and Qigong practice:

• May slow the loss of cardio-respiratory function due to aging.

• Is a social activity that encourages people of all ages to exercise because it is genuinely enjoyable.

• Is a very efficient (and therefore very effective) aerobic exercise.

• Exercises the cardiovascular system, increasing the heart rate moderately.

• Improves reflexes, uniting mind and body: 1. Fine-tuning muscles; 2. Stimulating right-left brain coordination; 3. Developing eye-hand coordination.

• Reduces stress and anxiety, promoting a sense of well-being.

A report from the Centers for Disease Control concludes that the leading cause of injury death for senior citizens is **FALLING.** In scientific studies conducted by well-known universities, such as Emory University in Atlanta, Taiji and Qigong practice has been proven to reduce the risk of falling.

And low-impact, weight-bearing exercise is recommended by many doctors to improve bone density. Taiji and Qigong are low-impact, weight-bearing exercises.

When I first work with someone who is new to this way of moving, I stress the importance of breathing—deep breathing. Try this: place one hand on your lower abdomen and one on your chest. Breathe normally for a few minutes. Now determine which hand moved the most, chest or abdomen? If you said chest, then your breathing is shallow and not reaching full capacity. This is important since our pulmonary (lung) capacity decreases every decade from our 20's on. If your lower hand moved more, that's a good start. Some of you who have been trained to sing already know what it means to do diaphragmatic breathing. There are two other stages of breathing. See the chart below. For the exercises in this book, Dan Tian breathing is the best. Reversed breathing requires special training.

Qigong Breathing Methods

Method	Inhalation	Exhalation	Purpose
Natural	Abdomen expands	Abdomen contracts	Establish good breathing habits and overall health
Dan Tian	Abdomen and lower back expand	Abdomen and lower back contract	Strengthen and cultivate dan tian qi, health and inner peace
Reversed	Abdomen contracts	Abdomen expands	Energize, strengthen diaphragm

The Tao of Breath
"Long breath, long life.
Short breath, short life.
No breath, death."
SAT CHUEN HON

Disclaimer

The opinions in this book are mine. The material included here is intended to be beneficial to your health. Many people have experienced improved health and other benefits. If you are unsure about whether this kind of exercise is right for you, consult your physician.

The author disclaims all responsibility for any liability, loss, or risk, personal or otherwise, which is incurred as a consequence, directly or indirectly, of the use and application of any of the contents in this book.

Section I: Hand Exercises

The hands are connected to all parts of the body through meridians. In acupuncture and traditional Chinese medicine, meridians are pathways in the body along which vital energy flows. There are fourteen such pathways. So when you massage the hands, you are massaging the body. Hand massage can be done virtually anywhere and any time.

"Like a Tree"   Ditan Park, 2008

1. Hand Exercises

Begin by grasping one hand with the other, with the thumb in the center of the palm. Press the thumb into the palm and spiral outward and around the palm (Figure 1). Continue with several rotations, being sure to touch all areas of the palm.

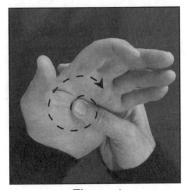
Figure 1

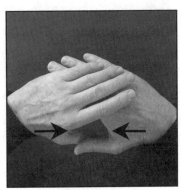
Figure 2

Next, join the hands (Figure 2) and massage the area between the index and thumb knuckles (Figure 3).

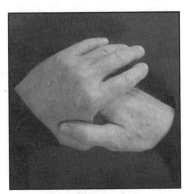
Figure 3

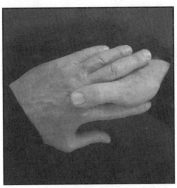
Figure 4

Then work your way over to and in between each pair of knuckles: index & middle (Figure 4), middle & ring, ring & little. *This is a loosening maneuver.*

Now tug, shake and pull each finger (Figures 5 & 6). You don't want to pull so hard that you crack the knuckles. *This is a lengthening, loosening exercise.*

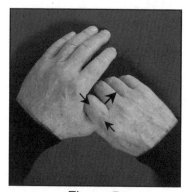

Figure 5

Figure 6

From there, massage the fingernail bed, the area between where the nail ends and the first knuckle (Figure 7). Place the index finger under the thumb while pressing with the thumb, in the area indicated by the arrows. Roll the thumb back and forth approximately 5 seconds.

Do each finger: index (Figure 8), middle, ring, and little.

Figure 7

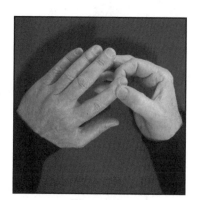

Figure 8

Pull the hand back with the palm, including the thumb, pushing the wrist forward in front of you (Figure 9). Then place your hand on top and pull the hand under while pushing the wrist forward (Figure 10). **Now repeat Figures 1-10 on the other hand.**

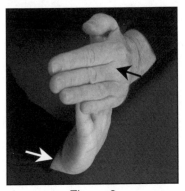
Figure 9

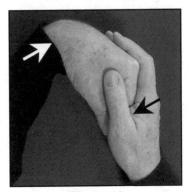
Figure 10

If the stretch is uncomfortable, do the stretches with your current range of motion and increase gradually until you can get the maximum stretch.

2. The Longevity Exercises

This is where it all began for me and is a personal favorite. Make a fist with the right hand and use the digits between the white and black arrows (Insert) to tap the center of the palm (Figures 11 & 12) of the left hand about 30 times, rapidly but not too hard, wrists loose. **Repeat on the other side, left tapping right.**

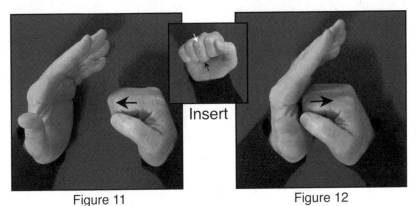
Insert

Figure 11　　　　　　　　Figure 12

Now tap the heels of the hands together (Figures 13 & 14), again, not too hard, approximately 30 times. Once you have done this a few times, you can eliminate the counting and approximate the duration of time.

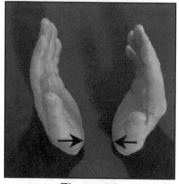
Figure 13

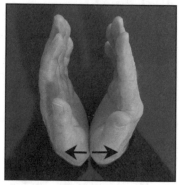
Figure 14

While you are doing these drills, stay loose, don't let your chest or your shoulders tighten up. If you start to tighten up, just drop your arms down to your sides and give them a shake.

Next, tap the sides of the hands together (Figures 15 &16). Keeping the elbows down low rather than raised up can help prevent muscle tension in the shoulders.

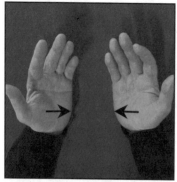
Figure 15

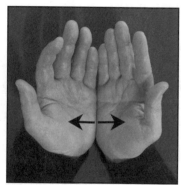
Figure 16

Now tap the area between the base of the thumb and where it connects to the wrist (Figures 17 & 18).

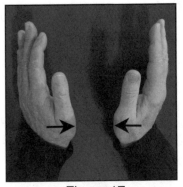
Figure 17

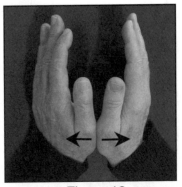
Figure 18

Drop your hands and shake your arms out.

Lace the fingers together (Figure 19). With an inward movement, bring the bases of the fingers together with enough force to make full contact with all bases without causing injury, then separate (Figure 20) and rapidly repeat 30 times. Pay attention to which index finger is on the bottom. Separate the fingers, rejoin with the other index finger on the bottom, and repeat.

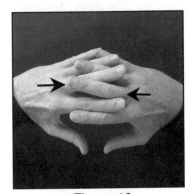
Figure 19

Figure 20

Join the left hand with the right (Figure 21) in the area known as the "tiger's mouth" (white double arrow). Tap in (Figure 22) and out 30 times. Then, separate the hands and rotate each a quarter turn counterclockwise, and repeat.

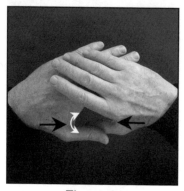

Figure 21

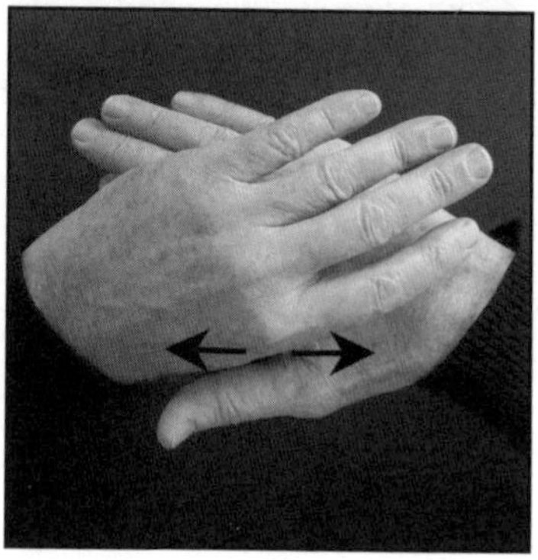

Figure 22

This is my favorite part: just hold your hands out after you have finished and let them float. Do you notice any sensations? I usually get a tingling feeling in my hands.

After that comes the finger rotations. Begin by extending both arms out in front of you at about chest height.

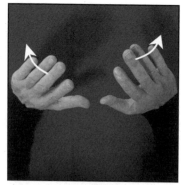

Figure 23

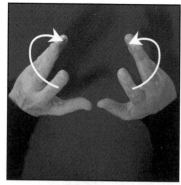

Figure 24

Then start the little fingers rotating, out and around, in the direction of the arrows (Figures 23 and 24) with all the fingers following.

Continue the rotation of the fingers (Figure 25) and the wrist (Figure 26)...

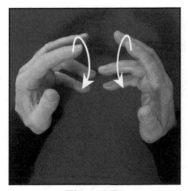 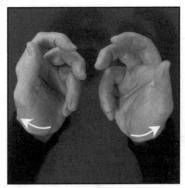

Figure 25   Figure 26

...until you can make a soft fist (Figure 27). **That completes one cycle.**

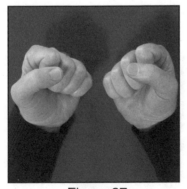 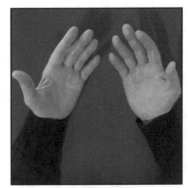

Figure 27   Figure 28

Now open your hands (Figure 28).

Using the same twining movement, leading out with the little fingers, curl the fingers inward (Figure 29). Continue in this direction (Figure 30).

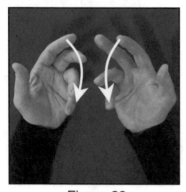

Figure 29

Figure 30

Rotate the wrists (Figure 31) as the fingers curl in. Finally, make a fist (Figure 32).

Repeat 5 more times (Figures 23-32), ending with the palms down in a fist. *Remember to keep the arms extended throughout the movements, and extend the little fingers out to begin the first rotation (Figure 24). The movements should be fluid and loose.*

Figure 31

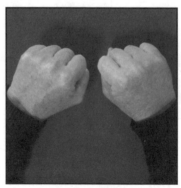

Figure 32

After the rotations, open the hands. Touch the thumb to the center of the palm (Figure 33). Then touch each finger one at a time, index (Figure 34), middle, ring and little, to the center of the palm.

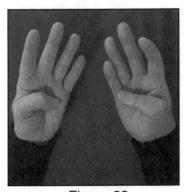

Figure 33

Figure 34

Then reverse, touching little, ring, middle, index and thumb.

With this next move, stretch the hands backward, while pushing the area indicated by the arrows in (Figure 35).

Relax the hands, moving in the opposite direction (Figure 36). **Repeat 5 times, in/out.**

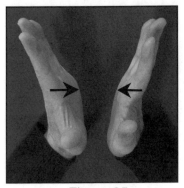

Figure 35

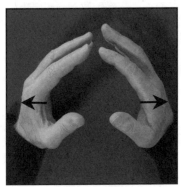

Figure 36

Wrist Rotations. Extend the arms out in front of you, at about chest height, keeping the shoulders relaxed. While extended, move the hands around in a circle, rotating at the wrists. Keep the hands parallel but not touching (Figure 37).

Figure 37

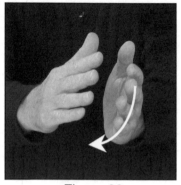
Figure 38

Continue in the same direction (Figures 38-40) until you are back at the beginning. Keep up the circular motion as one continuous movement. Do at least 5 rotations or more.

Just imagine you are drawing a circle with your middle fingers.

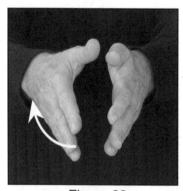
Figure 39

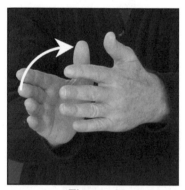
Figure 40

After at least 5 rotations, repeat in the opposite direction. If your hands don't move together while parallel, join them palm-to-palm and make the circles until you get used to it.

With the hands still facing each other, arms extended, move one hand down and one up (Figures 41 & 42), alternating at least 5 times or more. Imagine you have a softball or a ball of energy between your palms.

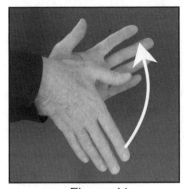
Figure 41

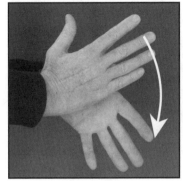
Figure 42

Now lower your hands. If you are seated, rest the backs of your hands on your knees. Then tap the thumb and index finger together quickly (Figures 43 & 44) about 30 times.

Figure 43

Figure 44

Continue with each fingertip, thumb/middle (Figure 45), thumb/ring, thumb/little, doing each 30 times.

Rumor has it that this exercise is good for your memory. So don't forget to do it.

Now it's time for a little fun. These hand games are also good for keeping your mind sharp, coordinating the right and left sides of the brain.

Figure 45

Figure 46

Begin by placing your hands together (Figure 46) and sliding them to the right (Figure 47), curling the outside fingers.

Then slide them to the left (Figure 48), curling the outside fingers. Start out slowly, being mindful of which fingers you are folding.

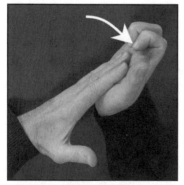

Figure 47

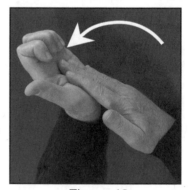

Figure 48

Once you've got it, try speeding up, moving like a windshield wiper.

This next one will bend your mind. Point your hands toward each other with the thumbs up (Figure 49). After that, make two fists (Figure 50). *Keep the elbows down.*

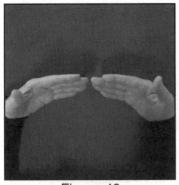

Figure 49

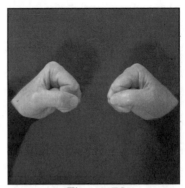

Figure 50

Repeat this alternating movement, point, fist, point, fist, until it's familiar.

Once you have that down, point to the right fist (Figure 51). Then point to the left fist (Figure 52). **Repeat a number of times.**

Figure 51

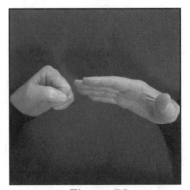

Figure 52

A fun variation to try is doing the back-and-forth routine in pairs, 1, 2, 1, 2, or triplicate, 1, 2, 3, 1, 2, 3. *Have fun.*

In this final hand game, you'll be challenged more than before. Just keep trying. First the easy part. Point the index fingers at each other with the thumbs up (Figure 53).

Figure 53

Figure 54

Then open the hands and place the thumbs in the center of the palms (Figure 54). Repeat this movement, point, extend, point, extend a number of times until you think you have it.

Now comes the best part. Using the left hand, point to the extension (Figure 55), then reverse (Figure 56). **Repeat back and forth a number of times.**

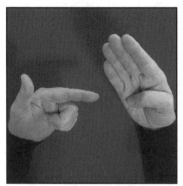
Figure 55

Figure 56

Looks easy until you try it. Once you can do these, have fun with your family and friends while sharpening their minds.

"Watermarks"   Ditan Park, 1998

"Fan Club"   Ditan Park, 1998

Section II: Self Massage

This section will include face washing, abdominal massage, ankle rotations, foot massage and the lower back massage.

3. Face Washing Massage

This can be done in bed, after the hand work, or in the shower; if you do it later in the day, be sure to wash your hands first. It feels good and helps relax and tone the facial muscles.

Figure 57

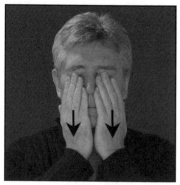

Figure 58

Start with the hands covering the face (Figure 57) and apply a gentle pressure. Wipe down (Figure 58).

Then back to covering the face (Figure 59) and wipe to the outside (Figure 60). **That is one set. Repeat 10 times: down, out, down, out.**

Figure 59

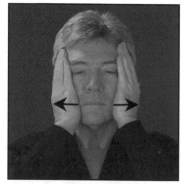

Figure 60

A woman once asked, "Shouldn't you wipe up to lift the face?" The answer is: No. The down motion trains the muscles to lift.

Now the area around the eyes will be addressed. Using the indicated part of the index finger (Insert), place between the eyebrows (Figure 61), apply a mild pressure and wipe across the eyebrows to the outside (Figure 62).

Figure 61

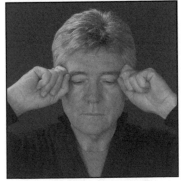
Figure 62

Then go under the eyes to the bridge of the nose (Figure 63), and wipe out (Figure 64).

Insert

That was one set. Repeat 10 times: over, under, over, under, etc.

Figure 63

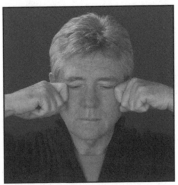
Figure 64

Finally, massage the sinuses. Using either the middle or index fingers, move up (Figure 65) and down (Figure 66) along the sinus passage.

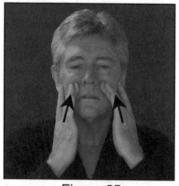

Figure 65

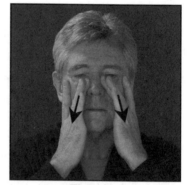

Figure 66

4. Abdominal Massage

Begin by placing the left hand on top of the right (Figure 67) for women, or the right hand on top of the left (Figure 68) for men.

Figure 67

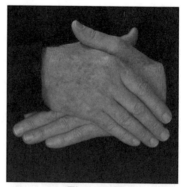

Figure 68

You are making a prenatal connection with the hand closest to your abdomen. The right (Figure 67) is female gender, the left (Figure 68) is male gender.

With the hands in the appropriate position, begin circling them clockwise, covering the entire abdomen (Figure 69) and continue around in a circle while applying a little pressure (Figures 70-72).

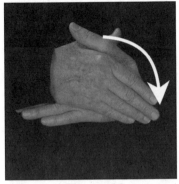

Figure 69

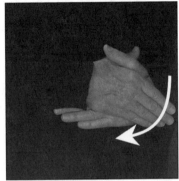

Figure 70

That was one set. Do this a total of 9 times in the same direction.

Then, do the same thing in the opposite direction, 9 times.

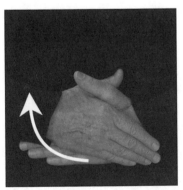

Figure 71

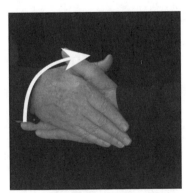

Figure 72

In case you are wondering, nine is the number of completion in Chinese culture.

5. Foot Massage

Reach down and grasp one ankle. Place the ankle on your opposite knee. Using your opposite hand, pull your toes down (Figure 73) and stretch the top of your foot. Then massage the arch of the foot with the other hand (Figure 73).

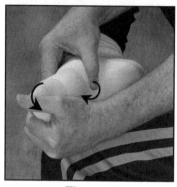
Figure 73

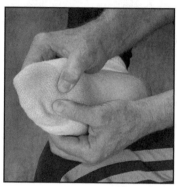
Figure 74

Use your thumbs to massage the ball of your foot (Figure 74). You can also work in between the toes and massage the toenail beds.

6. Ankle Rotations

Grab your ankle and rotate the foot (Figures 75 & 76) at least 5 times in the same direction, then in the opposite direction. Repeat with the other foot.

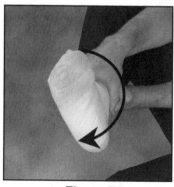
Figure 75

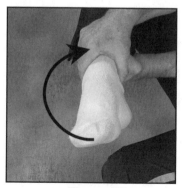
Figure 76

7. Lower Back Massage

Place both hands on the lower back, as high up as you can, and push in and down (Figure 77) to the lower back (Figure 78), repeating a few times.

Next place the thumbs on either side of the spine (Figure 79), as high as you can, and push in and down (Figure 80), repeating a couple of times.

Figure 77

Figure 78

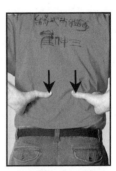

Figure 79

Finally, gently tap with the fists, moving up and down the spine (Figures 81 & 82). Repeat up and down a few times. The lower back work should be gauged by your comfort level.

My experience is that the lower back can easily tighten up while exercising, working, or doing any activity for that matter. Using my mind to relax the muscles, coupled with this massage technique, has helped reduce this problem.

Figure 80

Figure 81

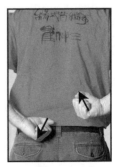

Figure 82

"Sword Storm"   Ditan Park, 1998

Section III: Warm-Up/Conditioning

These moves will loosen you up, firm you up, and generally make you feel good. No matter what your sport of choice, no matter where you are, this is a useful warm-up.

"Like This"   Ditan Park, 1998

8. Warm-Up Exercises

Begin by standing with the feet shoulder width apart, head lifted from the back, shoulders natural, arms slightly rounded, middle fingers on pant seams, knees soft, hips and waist loose (Figure 83), **Readiness Posture**.

Figure 83

Figure 84

Let the weight of the head carry you over (Figure 84) until you are hanging over (Figures 85 & 86). Breathe deeply; feel the small of the back expand as you inhale, release as you exhale. Shake the arms loose, shake the head "no," nod the head "yes."

Take another breath and as you exhale, slowly begin to roll up, stacking the vertebrae one at a time. The head is the last thing up.

Figure 85

Figure 86

45

After you stand up from hanging over, send the arms up over the head forming a triangle with the hands (Figure 87), bringing the elbows as close to the ears as you can.

Figure 87

Figure 88

Then release the arms down and out, opening the shoulders (Figure 89). **Repeat a few times.**

Follow that by alternating side to side (Figures 89 & 90), extending and releasing. **Repeat a few times.**

Figure 89

Figure 90

Now finish by simply reaching up with both hands (Figure 87), turn the palms out, and bring the arms down slowly (Figure 91).

Continue circling down (Figure 91). Be sure to release the shoulders and keep the head lifted.

Figure 91

Figure 92

Bring the arms in front of you (Figure 92) and, as they rise up (Figure 93), draw the breath in through the nose. Relax the lower abdomen (dan tian), allowing the expansion of both lower abdomen and lower back with the inhalation.

Once the arms reach the top (Figure 94), begin to exhale through the mouth by relaxing the lips and blowing out while circling the arms out, around, and down. Continue in a large circle (Figures 91-94). Work to synchronize your breath with the arm movement, inhaling up to the top and exhaling on the downward motion. **Do the circles at least 5 times in this direction**. *This is a good breath cleansing exercise.*

Figure 93

Figure 94

Now reverse the direction by swinging the arms back and around (Figure 95) while inhaling through the nose.

Figure 95

Figure 96

Continue around (Figures 96-98), beginning the exhalation at the top (Figure 97). Keep the shoulders loose throughout the drill. **Repeat at least 5 times in each direction.**

Figure 97

Figure 98

This type of breathing pattern is worth practicing regularly, first thing in the morning when it's critical to oxygenate the lungs. This can help prevent heart attacks, which occur more frequently in the early part of the day due to stress and a lack of oxygen.

While in the standing position, bring the tips of the fingers to the tops of the shoulders (Figure 99), then rotate the elbows forward (Figure 100) and around 9 times, then repeat in the opposite direction.

Figure 99

Figure 100

Temple Crunches are done by placing your fists on both sides of your head (Figure 101) and bringing the elbows together (Figure 102). These are great for opening up the back. **Repeat 9 times.**

Figure 101

Figure 102

Remember, if any of these stretches are uncomfortable and you can't modify them to ease your discomfort, omit that stretch temporarily and resume it at a better time. Consult a physician, if necessary, before continuing with anything that gives you discomfort.

I call this three-directional stretch **Press Back**. Begin with the arms in front of the chest, facing each other (Figure 103). Expand the elbows out and almost bounce them back while rotating the forearm 180° (Figure 104). Come back in (Figure 105,) stacking the arms with the other on top, then back out (Figure 106).

Figure 103

Figure 104

Catching the rhythm and bounce of this drill is important to the success of the movement. The count so far, on an 8-count drill is, 1, 2. 1 is out (Figure 104), bounce, rotate, in (Figure 105), 2 is out (Figure 106) bounce.

Figure 105

Figure 106

Extend the arms in front of you with the palms up (Figure 107) and swing them out and back (Figure 108), bouncing lightly, releasing and allowing the arms to spring forward and bounce back a second time.

Figure 107

Figure 108

After the second bounce back, one arm goes up while the other goes down (Figure 110) with the same bounce and spring as in the previous direction, also twice.

Then repeat on the opposite side (Figure 111), same 2 count, same energy. **Repeat the sequence (Figures 103-111) 4 more times for a total of 5 repetitions. This is an 8-count drill, 8-counts per repetition.**

Figure 110

Figure 111

With the feet shoulder width apart (whenever you are standing, unless otherwise specified, the feet should be at this distance), place the hands on the lower back (Insert) and begin rotating the hips and waist around in a circle (Figures 112-115).

Figure 112

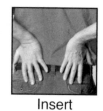

Insert

Figure 113

Continue circling around for at least 9 rotations, then repeat in the opposite direction. Keep the knees slightly bent, head lifted from the back, feet planted on the floor.

Figure 114

Figure 115

Place both hands on the knees and rotate them in opposite directions (Figures 116 &117), then reverse the directions. **Do both directions at least 9 times.**

Figure 116

Figure 117

Doing the wrists and ankles can be awkward and fun. Rotate the wrists and right ankle in the same direction (Figures 118 & 119), then reverse the direction. Repeat, rotating the left ankle in each direction.

Do this in each direction at least 9 times.

It helps to get the shoe on point, keeping the ankle loose, as well as the wrists.

I've yet to see anyone who doesn't feel a little inelegant doing this one at first.

Figure 118

Figure 119

I call this **The Wave**. It's a rising and falling action (Figures 120-123). Once you get it going, try to reverse it.

Figure 120

Figure 121

The main thing is to keep it loose. I use the word "loose" more than "relaxed." Relaxed is the end result, loose and lively is the vehicle.

Figure 122

Figure 123

9. Eight-Step Hip Exercise

Hip work is a good break for the feet, and good for the hips.
Begin with the feet shoulder width apart, hands behind the
head (Figure 124).

You put your right foot out with the toe raised (Figure 125 &
Insert 1) but not flexed.

Figure 124

Insert 1

Figure 125

Step back (Figure 126). Then put the left foot out (Figure 127)
and step back (Figure 128). **Repeat a total of 8 times,
4 for each foot.**

Figure 126

Figure 127

Figure 128

Put the right heel back with the toes raised (Figure 129 & Insert 2), then step forward (Figure 130).

Figure 129

Insert 2

Figure 130

Then put the left heel back with toes raised (Figure 131), and return to the original position (Figure 132).

Repeat a total of 8 times, 4 times for each foot.

Figure 131

Figure 132

Sometimes, to help remember a move, I'll give it a name, like **Hackie Sack**. This next move is like kicking a hackie sack with the side of the foot (Figure 133).

Repeat on the other side (Figure 134). That's 1, 2. Now repeat each foot in succession, counting to 8.

| Figure 133 | Figure 134 | Figure 135 |

The final move is called **Sexy Knee**. Roll the knee in, rise up on the ball of the foot (Figure 135), and rotate out (Figure 136).

Repeat on the other side (Figures 137 & 138). **Do 6 more for a total of 8.**

Now try the entire set again. For deeper benefits, increase the number of repetitions.

| Figure 136 | Figure 137 | Figure 138 |

10. Fan the Air

This next drill can be done standing, sitting or lying down. Be sure to turn the whole torso. Do not just move the arms.

Figure 139

Figure 140

Figure 141

Begin with the arms out in front of you (Figure 139) and turn to the left, 45°, raising the hands to shoulder height (Figure 140). As you turn 90° to the right, drop and raise the arms 4 times. This should bring you to the opposite side at a 45° angle (Figures 141-144).

Figure 142

Figure 143

Figure 144

Now, dropping and raising the arms 4 more times, turn 90°
back to the left (Figures 144-148). This takes you back to the
starting point.

Figure 145

Figure 146

Figure 147

If you're feeling energetic, repeat the cycle, ending on the left.

Pick Up the Bucket. Now, as you raise the arms (Figure 149),
imagine that you are grabbing and picking up a bucket,
making two fists (Figure 150). From this position, start turning
the waist, keeping the arms in front of you.

Figure 148

Figure 149

Figure 150

Continue turning (Figure 151) to the opposite side (Figure 152), facing at a 45° angle.

Open the fists (Figure 152) quickly, dropping the arms down, **Dropping the Bucket** (Figure 153). Then return up (Figure 154), in a grabbing action, and turn (Figure 155) to the other side (Figure 156). Drop the bucket.

| Figure 151 | Figure 152 | Figure 153 |

Repeat a few more times. Remember to turn the entire torso and not just move the arms; this is a waist turning exercise.

| Figure 154 | Figure 155 | Figure 156 |

With this kind of extension of the arms, keep the shoulders loose.

11. Chop/Release

Place your left arm in front of you. With the right hand raised above the left-hand fingers (Figure 157), chop down in front of the knuckles (Figure 158). Chop with the edge of your fingers, not the side of your hand. It's meant to be a loose chop, not a karate chop.

Figure 157

Figure 158

Figure 159

Next, chop down on the wrist (Figures 159-160).

Figure 160

Figure 161

Figure 162

Then chop 1/3 of the way up the arm (Figures 161-162).

61

After that, chop at the elbow (Figures 163-164). Then repeat the sequence on the other arm.

Figure 163

Figure 164

Figure 165

To finish the sequence, form the hands like tiger claws (Figure 165), just below the chest. That's 1. Then, in two moves, extend the arms fully forward (Figures 166 and 167). That's 2, 3.

Finally, rotate both hands in opposite directions (like turning two knobs). Shake the head "no". And, with loose lips, make a goofy sound (Figure 168). **Repeat the sequence another time.**

Figure 166

Figure 167

Figure 168

Rounding out the set is the HU! Drill. It's called that because you say HU! (the Chinese word for Tiger) with the thrust. Start with the hands in the tiger claw position at chest height (Figure 169). Strike across with the left hand (Figure 170), thrust over the left with the right hand (Figure 171) and say HU!

| Figure 169 | Figure 170 | Figure 171 |

Separate the hands (Figure 172), bring them down (Figure 169). Then, right strike (Figure 173), left thrust (Figure 174), with another HU! Separate the hands (Figure 172), bring them down (Figure 169). Got it? **Repeat**.

| Figure 172 | Figure 173 | Figure 174 |

These last drills (Figures 139-174) are great for raising the spirit.

"Qigong Anyone"   Ditan Park, 1998

Section IV: Qigong

This final section includes three Standing Qigongs and four Crane Qigongs. By "standing," I mean they are done standing in place. The four Crane Qigongs include footwork. If you cannot stand, you can still benefit from the Qigongs by performing the upper body movements and breathing patterns. You can do these exercises sitting or lying down.

"Qigong Everyone"   Ditan Park, 1998

12. Standing Qigongs

The standing Qigongs are done in place. The first one requires learning a pattern, the Taiji circle and its mirror image. Study the illustration below for a while, then move your hands in the directions of the arrows.

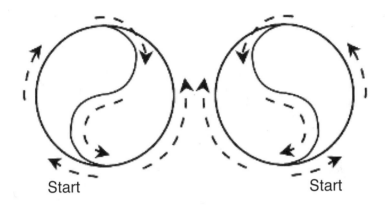

Start   Start

Begin in the Readiness Posture, feet shoulder width apart (Figure 175). Check the stance width by turning one of your feet in until the toe touches the other heel (Insert), then rotate back out to feet parallel. Place your hands in front of you, just above waist height, and follow the arrows (Figure 176).

Figure 175   Insert   Figure 176

Once both hands have circled up to the top (Figure 177), at about shoulder height, begin the two half circles, as shown, to the center of the circle.

Figure 177

Figure 178

Then do the two half circles from the center of the circle in the opposite direction (Figure 178) to the bottom of the circle.

Now from the bottom position (Figure 179), circle inward to finish the other side of the circle. Continue around (Figure 180) to the beginning position (Figure 176).

Figure 179

Figure 180

Practice this until you are familiar with the movement. In the actual drill, your hands will be extended down and in front of you.

68

The Complete Drill. From the Readiness Posture (Figure 181) expand out (Figure 182) and lift the hands in front of you (Figure 183), as if laying your hands on a table. **Maintain an openness and roundness, expanding out as if you are filling up with fluid in the upper torso; keep the shoulders down.**

| Figure 181 | Figure 182 | Figure 183 |

The breathing throughout this Qigong should be natural, in and out through the nose. The movement is slow and continuous; keep it smooth. Lightly touch the tip of the tongue on the ridge behind the upper teeth to help keep the mouth salivated.

Move through this Qigong as if moving through a liquid slightly denser than water, but no effort is needed to move through it.

| Figure 184 | Figure 185 | Figure 186 |

Raise the hands to chest height (Figure 184), then turn them over (Figure 185). Now slowly, gently push down (Figure 186), keeping the arms slightly rounded.

Now rotate just the wrists (Figure 187) until the hands are pointed out (Figure 188) and lay them back into the sides (Figure 189), i.e., return to the Readiness Posture.

| Figure 187 | Figure 188 | Figure 189 |

Expand back out (Figure 190), opening the hands (Figure 191). Only this time you are going to make the Taiji Circle and its mirror image (Figure 192). If you get confused, go back to the diagram on page 67. Once you've completed the two circles, you'll be at Figure 188 again. To finish one cycle, just lay the hands back in to the sides (Figure 189).

Repeat the entire form for 2-7 minutes. Keep the hands low and the arms rounded.

| Figure 190 | Figure 191 | Figure 192 |

This Qigong takes a little practice, so be patient and persistent. Most people say it is one of their favorites.

Begin this next Qigong in the Readiness Posture (Figure 189, page 70) and open out (Figure 193). At the same time, sink down until the knees are somewhere between the end of your shoelaces and the end of your shoe (Insert), but no further. **Hold this sunken position throughout the drill.**

Figure 193

Insert

Figure 194

As you raise your arms (Figure 194), inhale through the nose, drawing the breath into the dan tian area (see page 14). **Remember to place the tip of the tongue on the ridge behind the upper teeth.**

At the top of the move, drop the elbows, releasing the shoulders (Figure 195) and lower the arms down while exhaling through the mouth (gently part the lips and blow). Raise the arms again (Figure 196) and repeat the exercise for 2-7 minutes. **To finish, lower the arms to the starting position and straighten the legs.**

Figure 195

Figure 196

The last standing Qigong is done by moving from the Readiness Posture (Figure 197), expanding out and sinking down to the knee-over-shoe position (Figure 198), extending the hands up and out (Figure 199). Just blend it into one motion. Inhale through the nose as you raise the hands to shoulder height. Exhale through the mouth as you follow the three points of release: 1. Shoulders (Figure 201); 2. Elbows (Figure 201); 3. Wrists (Figure 201). Figures 200 & 202 show this movement from the front. When the hands reach waist height, raise the arms again (Figure 199).

Figure 197

Figure 198

Figure 199

Repeat for 2-7 minutes. The two Qigongs done in the sunken position should be done on the following schedule: Month 1, sink down a little and do the movements for 2-3 minutes; Month 2, sink a little more, end of shoelaces, for 3-5 minutes; Month 3, sink to knees at the end of shoes, for 5-7 min. Adjust these routines to suit your schedule.

Figure 200

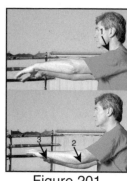
Figure 201

Figure 202

13. Crane Circles the Earth and Returns

Practice the footwork first. From the Readiness Posture (Figure 203), shift the weight to the right foot. Step out with the left foot at a 45° angle onto the heel, knee slightly bent (Figure 204).

Figure 203

Figure 204

Figure 205

Shift the weight forward (Figure 205) raising the back heel.

You will be shifting back and forth like this during this form.

To finish the left side and start the right side, shift your weight to the right leg (Figure 206), and step back with the left (Figure 207). Shift to the left foot and step out with the right (Figure 208).

Figure 206

Figure 207

Figure 208

Now practice the arm movements. Begin with the arms at your side (Figure 209). Lift the arms in front of you (Figure 210), while inhaling through the nose. Continue lifting the arms (Figure 211).

Figure 209

Figure 210

Figure 211

From the arms extended position (Figure 212), begin exhaling while lowering the arms.

At shoulder height, make two fists (Figure 213), and continue to the waist (Figure 214).

Figure 212

Figure 213

Figure 214

To continue the circular movement, open the hands, begin to inhale, and repeat Figures 210-214. Repeat this until it becomes familiar.

Once you've done one direction, then you go in the other. With the fists at waist height (Figure 215), inhale and raise them toward the shoulders. At shoulder height (Figure 216), open the hands and continue up (Figure 217).

Figure 215

Figure 216

Figure 217

At the top, begin to exhale through the mouth, circling the arms out and down (Figure 218) to about waist height (Figure 219).

Keep circling the arms by repeating Figures 215-219.

Figure 218

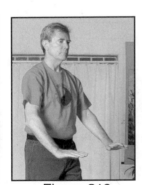
Figure 219

Figure 220

To finish, simply bring the hands back to the starting position (Figure 220). Practice each direction, then put it all together.

Once you have practiced the leg work and the arm movements, you're ready to put them together. From the Readiness Posture (Figure 221), shift your weight to your right foot as you step out with your left foot at a 45° angle (Figure 222).

Figure 221

Figure 222

Figure 223

As you shift your weight forward, lower the left foot, raise the right heel, swing the arms out and up while inhaling through the nose (Figure 223).

When your arms reach the top of the circle (Figure 224), begin to shift back and exhale through the mouth.

Figure 224

Figure 225

Figure 226

When your hands reach shoulder height, make them into soft fists (Figure 225), and lower them to your waist (Figure 226). To continue, open the hands, shift forward, inhale and continue around, repeating Figures 223-226. **Do at least 5 rotations.**

Now reverse the direction. Starting from the fists at your waist (Figure 227), extend up to shoulder height, shift forward while inhaling (Figure 228). At shoulder height, open the fists, extending out and up (Figure 229).

| Figure 227 | Figure 228 | Figure 229 |

This point of extension should also include lifting from the top of the head, lengthening the spine. Just don't force it.

As you continue down (Figures 230 & 231), remember to exhale.

| Figure 230 | Figure 231 | Figure 232 |

To keep the cycle going, bring the hands to the waist and repeat Figures 227-231. **Do this at least 5 times**. When you've finished, bring your hands to the sides and shift your weight to the right foot (Figure 232).

Now that you've completed the Qigong on one side, do it on the other side. To make the transition: with your arms at your sides (Figure 233), shift your weight to your right foot and step back with the left (Figure 234).

| Figure 233 | Figure 234 | Figure 235 |

From this position, you can do one of two things. You can return to the Readiness Posture (Figure 235), or you can blend into the other side by shifting your weight to the left foot and stepping out with the right to the 45° angle (Figure 236).

The first way gives you a moment to rest. Either way is fine. To continue, shift your weight forward, inhale and lift the arms (Figure 237). **Do Figures 223-226 & 227-231 each 5 times.**

| Figure 236 | Figure 237 |

To finish, bring your arms to your sides, shift your weight to your left foot, step back with the right to the beginning position (Figure 235).

14. Crane Lifts Up and Returns

Practice the footwork first. Even though the footwork of this Qigong begins the same as the previous one, it's slightly different. From the Readiness Posture (Figure 238), shift the weight to the right foot and step out with the left at a 45° angle. Shifting the weight forward, raise the back heel (Figure 239).

Figure 238

Figure 239

Figure 240

Then shift back, raising the front foot (Figure 240).

From there, shift forward onto the left foot and bring the right foot up to shoulder width apart (Figure 241).

Figure 241

Figure 242

Figure 243

Finally, shift right and step back with the left foot (Figure 242). Shift left, bringing the right foot back to the beginning position (Figure 243).

Now practice the arm movements. From the stepped-out 45° position, raise the arms out in front of you, letting the hands hang loosely down (Figure 244), while inhaling. Continue up (Figure 245). Drop the elbows down, then the wrists follow while exhaling (Figure 246).

| Figure 244 | Figure 245 | Figure 246 |

While continuing down (Figure 247), the palms are out. Be careful not to flex the wrists too sharply. *You always want to allow the optimum path for unrestricted circulation.*

| Figure 247 | Figure 248 | Figure 249 |

At just below waist height (Figure 248), begin inhaling, the hands rise up to the push position (Figure 249).

Continue with the push (Figure 250), inhaling as you extend. At the end of the push, extend the hands (Figure 251). *Don't overextend the arms.*

Figure 250

Figure 251

Figure 252

Now using the three-point release from Figure 201 on page 72, exhale through the mouth while releasing the shoulders, dropping the elbows, and allowing the wrists to follow as you pull the hands down (Figure 252).

Continue arcing down (Figure 253) to just below waist height (Figure 254).

Figure 253

Figure 254

Figure 255

To finish this side, bring your hands to your sides (Figure 255).

Combining the upper and lower movements, step out with the left foot from the **Readiness Posture** (Figure 256) to the 45° position. Shift forward (Figure 257), raise the arms (Figure 258), and inhale.

Figure 256

Figure 257

Figure 258

Shift back, drop the shoulders, then the elbows (Figure 259).

Figure 259

Exhale as you come down. Imagine a small resistance as you move, but no effort is needed move through it.

Figure 260

Figure 261

Figure 262

Stay in the shifted-back position as you pull down (Figure 260) to your hips (Figure 261). Now step the right foot up to shoulder width apart, knees bent, palms in the push position at the waist (Figure 262). Be careful not to flex the wrists here; keep the channel open.

Push up and forward (Figure 263). Inhale on the push. Be careful not to overextend. Extend the hands (Figure 264), release the shoulders, drop the elbows (Figure 265), and exhale while pulling down (Figure 266).

| Figure 263 | Figure 264 | Figure 265 |

Let the wrists follow to hip height (Figure 267), straightening the legs at the same time. Bring your hands to your sides (Figure 268) and follow the footwork in Figures 242 & 243 on page 79. This will bring you back to the starting point.

To begin the other side from Figure 268, shift your weight to the left and step out with the right foot. The upper body is the same as Figures 257-268. Remember that you step out to a 45° angle.

| Figure 266 | Figure 267 | Figure 268 |

As you practice these movements daily, they will become more fluid, smoother, and more refined. Alternate from side to side, doing each side at least 5 times.

15. Crane Shows Intent

Practice the footwork first. From the Readiness Posture (Figure 269), shift the weight to the right foot and step out with the left at a 45° angle (Figure 270). Shift the weight forward and raise the back heel (Figure 271).

Figure 269

Figure 270

Figure 271

When you shift back, raise up the heel (Figure 272) of the left foot.

You will be moving back and forth between Figures 271 & 272 for the duration of the drill.

Figure 272

Figure 273

Figure 274

When you have finished, step the right foot up to shoulder width apart (Figure 273). To make the transition to the other side, shift your weight to the right, step back with the left (Figure 274), and step out to the 45° angle with the right.

The arm movement is relatively easy. From the Readiness Posture (Figure 275), step left to the 45° position, right palm down, left palm up and extended (Figure 276).

Figure 275

Figure 276

Figure 277

As you shift forward, the right hand passes over the left (Figure 277).

Continue extending the right hand, turning the torso slightly to the left; and, pull the left hand down to your side, palm down (Figures 278 and 279).

Figure 278

Figure 279

Figure 280

Then pull down the right hand while bringing up the left (Figure 280).

The hands pass each other (Figure 281). Draw the right hand into a fist as you extend the left out in front (Figure 282).

Figure 281

Figure 282

Figure 283

In this Qigong, you keep repeating the moves (Figures 276-282).

When you have finished the drill, extend the arms (Figure 283), and do the three-point release (see Figure 201 on page 72). Bring the arms down and back to your sides (Figures 284 and 285).

Figure 284

Figure 285

Practice the arm movements before you put your feet under them. Remember to keep the head lifted from the back.

Combining the upper and lower body movements should be easy by now. From the Readiness Posture (Figure 286), shift your weight to the right foot and step out with the left at 45°. Extend your left hand out with the palm up and bring the right hand with palm down up to the left hand (Figures 287 and 288). Start to inhale.

| Figure 286 | Figure 287 | Figure 288 |

As you shift forward, the two hands pass each other (Figure 288). Extend the right hand all the way up and out, as the left palm moves down to your side (Figure 289). *Remember to turn slightly to the left, inhaling fully. Don't force the movement or the breath.*

Now shift back onto the right foot, pull the right hand down as you bring the left out so the hands pass each other. Begin to exhale (Figure 290).

| Figure 289 | Figure 290 | Figure 291 |

Take your weight back onto the right leg as the waist turns to the right (Figure 291). The left hand has gone from palm down to palm on edge in the transition; as the hands pass by each other, the palms are facing each other (Figures 290 and 291).

Finish the first move by extending the left hand out, palm on edge.
The right hand is in a fist, palm up, at your waist, and the left heel is
raised up (Figure 292). Exhale fully during this move. That's
one repetition.

| Figure 292 | Figure 293 | Figure 294 |

Move into the next repetition by following Figures 293-297.
Remember to inhale as you move from Figure 292 to Figure 294
and to exhale as you move from Figure 294 to Figure 297.

| Figure 295 | Figure 296 | Figure 297 |

After you get the moves down you'll catch the rhythm. **Repeat at
least 3 more times for a total of 5.**

Once you've finished your repetitions, you need to close. This is done by stepping up to feet shoulder width apart and extending your arms out in front of you (Figure 298). Then using the three-point release, bring the arms down, straighten your knees, and bring your hands to your sides (Figures 299 and 300).

Figure 298

Figure 299

Figure 300

Now do the other side. Begin by shifting your weight to your right leg and stepping back with the left (Figure 301).

Shift to the left leg and step out with the right foot to the 45° angle, left palm up and right palm down (Figure 302).

Figure 301

Figure 302

Figure 303

Then shift your weight forward to the right foot and continue pulling down with the right hand while extending the left hand (Figure 303).

Since this Qigong is not as symmetrical as the others, I'm showing you both sides. The right hand is palm down (Figure 304). The palms are facing each other as they pass (Figures 305 & 306).

Figure 304

Figure 305

Figure 306

The left fist is facing up.

Figure 307

The right hand is on edge (Figure 307).

Do a total of 5 repetitions. Step up and close (Figures 308-310).

Figure 308

Figure 309

Figure 310

16. Crane Takes Flight

Practice the footwork first. From the Readiness Posture (Figure 311), lightly set the left heel forward (Figure 312). Slowly shift the weight forward, raising the right heel (Figure 313).

Figure 311

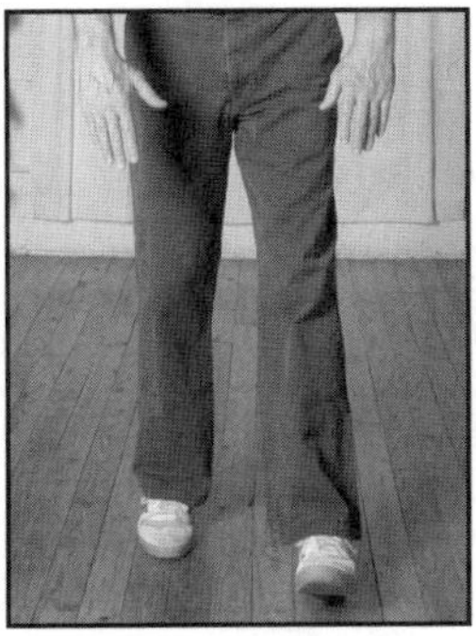

Figure 313

Figure 312

Then shift back (Figure 314), shift forward (Figure 315), placing all of your weight on the left foot, and extend your right foot behind you pointing the foot (Figure 316).

Practicing this balancing act could save your life. Having good balance, especially as you get older, is essential to your well-being. Most injuries that happen to elderly people are due to loss of balance. You can leave your back toe touching the floor at first. It won't be long before you can lift it.

Figure 314

Figure 315

Figure 316

Bring the right leg down (Figure 317). When your weight has settled in, shift back and raise the left foot (Figure 318), then bring it back to the starting point (Figure 319).

That is the basic footwork for one side. Practice for a while until it becomes familiar.

Figure 317

Figure 318

Figure 319

The other side is a mirror image. From the **Readiness Posture**, (Figure 320) step forward with the right foot (Figure 321).

Keeping the ankle released, so the heel sets out lightly, reduces unnecessary tension in the ankle and foot. Once you have experienced this more released step, you'll notice the difference.

Shift forward raising the left heel (Figure 322).

Figure 320

Figure 321

Figure 322

Shift back (Figure 323), shift forward (Figure 324) until your weight is centered over the right foot. Raise the back leg pointing the foot (Figure 325).

You will be extending in all directions at the same time.

| Figure 323 | Figure 324 | Figure 325 |

Whenever you extend the body, the movement is expanded but not forced. Balance and finesse go a long way here.

Finish by lowering the extended leg (Figure 324), allowing the weight to return to the back leg so you can easily pick up the front foot (Figure 324), and resume the original position (Figure 325).

| Figure 323 | Figure 324 | Figure 325 |

Now practice the arm movements. From the readiness posture (Figure 326), raise the arms up, right over left, if you step out with the left foot (Figure 327). *The hands in Figure 327 are a typical crane hand position. To form the crane hand, reach down with your fingertips as if you were plucking something from the air. With fingertips together, pointing down, raise the wrists.*

| Figure 326 | Figure 327 | Figure 328 |

Raise your arms up over your head (Figure 328). From Figure 326-328 is the inhalation.

Open the hands (Figure 329). The wrists stay together as you bring the hands down, while exhaling.

Extend both arms out to the sides and a little behind you (Figure 330).

| Figure 329 | Figure 330 | Figure 331 |

Now bring the arms forward again, right over left (Figure 331).

Raise the arms over the head (Figure 332). *This may seem repetitive, but the footwork varies. For now, just get loose with the movement.*

Open your hands (Figure 333). That's right, this is where you begin the exhalation.

| Figure 332 | Figure 333 | Figure 334 |

Continue to pull down with the hands extended (Figure 334), but not tense.

To finish the first side, return to the beginning posture (Figure 335).

The other side is a mirror image, but let's use it to review the moves.

| Figure 335 | Figure 336 | Figure 337 |

Raise the arms up with hands in the crane position, left over right (Figure 336), until they are overhead (Figure 337).

Open the hands (Figure 338). This is where you begin to exhale. Just relax the lips and blow, slowly. The duration of the breath should follow the full extension (Figure 339).

While drawing the breath in through the nose, form the hands in the crane position (Figure 340).

| Figure 338 | Figure 339 | Figure 340 |

As you rise up (Figure 341), keep the chest open by keeping the arms rounded and the shoulders loose.

This is where you start to internalize the movement, feeling the difference between tense and relaxed. Each time you run through the routine, refine the movement and let the breath drop down.

| Figure 341 | Figure 342 | Figure 343 |

Finish by opening the hands (Figure 342), and bringing them down to the closing position (Figure 343).

To put it all together, start from the Readiness Posture (Figure 344). Shift your weight to the right foot and step out with the left. As your arms begin to rise, inhale through the nose (Figure 345). Cross the right arm over the left with crane hands and shift your weight forward to the left foot (Figure 346) as your right heel rises up.

Figure 344

Figure 345

Figure 346

Continue raising your arms until they are over your head (Figure 347). Now open your hands and begin to shift back while exhaling through the mouth (Figure 348).

The arms should move smoothly down as your weight settles into your right foot and the left foot rises up (Figure 349).

Figure 347

Figure 348

Figure 349

Be patient and persistent. Don't force anything. Just allow the movement to become you.

Keep exhaling slowly as you separate your arms out to the side (Figure 350) and begin to shift forward (Figure 351). As you lift the right foot, fully extend in all directions (Figure 352). Hold for a couple of seconds.

| Figure 350 | Figure 351 | Figure 352 |

Draw the breath in as you lower your right foot. Cross the right arm over the left, hands in crane position (Figure 353), and shift back.

Extend the arms over your head with your weight on the back foot (Figure 354). *When you are at these extremes it's important to keep the arms rounded with the shoulders loose.*

Now open your hands, start lowering the arms, and begin exhaling (Figure 355).

| Figure 353 | Figure 354 | Figure 355 |

Keep pulling down (Figure 356), bringing all of your weight to the right leg. Step back with the left foot as your arms continue down (Figure 357) until you are back in the beginning position (Figure 358).

| Figure 356 | Figure 357 | Figure 358 |

That completes one side. You will be alternating from one side to the other.

Begin the other side by shifting your weight to the left foot and stepping out with the right foot (Figure 359).

This time cross the left arm over the right as you rise up; your arms lift with the weight shift (Figure 360). The weight shifts to the right (Figure 361). *Remember to inhale deeply into the dan tian.*

| Figure 359 | Figure 360 | Figure 361 |

This stretch is long and loose, characteristic of Crane Style Qigong. From the fully extended position (Figure 362), open the hands to begin the exhalation (Figure 363), and shift your weight back as the hands descend (Figure 364).

| Figure 362 | Figure 363 | Figure 364 |

As your arms come down, transfer your weight forward to the right foot (Figure 365).

Get set up (Figure 366) for the full extension (Figure 367).

By now you should be getting more familiar with this style of movement.

| Figure 365 | Figure 366 | Figure 367 |

This moment of full extension is suspended, the end of the breath, a lightness of being.

Step down, shift back, raise the arms left over right, and draw the breath in (Figure 368). Shift back and stretch up (Figure 369), then release the hands (Figure 370) at the beginning of the final exhalation.

Figure 368

Figure 369

Figure 370

As you come down (Figure 371), get your right foot grounded so you can easily step back (Figure 372).

Close in the usual fashion (Figure 373).

That completes 1 cycle. Repeat 4 more times on each side for a total of 5.

Figure 371

Figure 372

Figure 373

Practice daily to receive the full benefits. I hope you enjoy these exercises as much as I do.

"At The Center"   Ditan Park, 2008

Order Form

To obtain additional copies of: **Breath Energy Work**
Exercises for the Mind & Body
by Michael Holland

Send check or money order
made payable to: Breath Energy Work
323 Ridgeland Ave.
Decatur, GA 30030

For the amount of: $19.95 + $5.75 for shipping & handling (1 copy)
$19.95 + $2.00 for each additional book

Please send me (   ) copy/copies of your book $_____

Shipping and handling   _____

Georgia residents add 7% sales tax   _____

Total   _____
(International orders, email mholland108@gmail.com for shipping fees.)

Name_____

Address_____

City, State Zip _____

To order online (PayPal) go to: breathenergywork.com

Make a copy of this page and include with your payment.
Make a copy of the completed form for your records.